THE MISSING
MINISTER

Religious and Moral Education Press
An imprint of Chansitor Publications Ltd,
a wholly owned subsidiary of Hymns Ancient & Modern Ltd
St Mary's Works, St Mary's Plain
Norwich, Norfolk NR3 3BH

First published 1995

ISBN 1 85175-056-8

The characters and the companies that appear in this story
are entirely fictitious.

Note
Information on how this book can be used in schools is provided on
pages 90 to 92.

Designed and typeset by Topics Visual Information, Exeter

Illustrations by Clive Wakfer

Printed in Great Britain by BPC Wheatons Ltd, Exeter
for Chansitor Publications Ltd, Norwich

THE MISSING
MINISTER

TERENCE COPLEY

RMEP

ACKNOWLEDGEMENTS

This is the fourth book in a series that grew out of a quip. To Mary Mears of RMEP, by now a recidivist of RE crime books, thanks, and more especially for editorial support and suspicious suggestions throughout the project. To the youngsters who examined this case in draft stages and gave their own comments on its viability as a new RE crime story, thanks.

I was born into a Nonconformist cradle and acquired chapel life by osmosis. In those days you were still 'chapel' or 'church' in the villages (and the Norman Conquest seemed recent ...). My understanding of Baptist churches in particular owes much to the writings of and about those two Victorian Baptist giants John Clifford and Charles Haddon Spurgeon, and to the living Baptist chapels and chapel folk in Godmanchester and Huntingdon, Cambridgeshire; Duffield and Belper, Derbyshire; and Priory Street, York. Mary Cotes, one of the ministers of the South Street Baptist Church, Exeter, provided insider information on the crime and corrected some of the less authentic details in the case. Her calm response when I first telephoned as a total stranger to ask her to meet me to discuss a crime in which a female Baptist minister was apparently a victim of kidnapping was remarkable. Perhaps she receives calls like that every day. But the help she provided was generous and invaluable.

Thanks are also due to the pastor of the Metropolitan Tabernacle, Dr Peter Masters, for providing two illustrations from *Sword and Trowel* of C. H. Spurgeon, on which the drawing on page 26 is based. The illustration across the bottom of the pages 38 and 39 is based on genuine extracts from the *Baptist Times*.

Coded use of religious material is real and not fiction. In the Second World War, soldiers writing home were not allowed for security reasons to state where they were (in case their letters fell into enemy hands) and letters were strictly censored, by an official who passed them, or blacked out sections or confiscated the whole letter. In March 1942 one soldier, D. Alan Copley, wrote a letter from *somewhere* to his wife. In it he said, 'We had a meeting with the padre [army chaplain] yesterday to discuss hymns. We thought that number 611 was very good, especially the last line of verse two. What do you think?' The censor reading the letter couldn't know which hymn-book was referred to, but Alan Copley's wife knew, as they were both Methodists. She looked up hymn 611, which started with the words 'Lead us, heavenly Father, lead us'. The last line of verse two says, 'Through the desert thou didst go.' She knew from this – in 1942 – that her husband was in the North Africa desert war. Real religious code!

The reference to Cave Adullam Chapel (page 20) is also genuine and not a Copley hidden joke. This gloriously named 'cause', to use old Nonconformist language, really exists and can be visited along with its neat burial ground at Beeches Road, Blackheath, West Midlands. It is part of a small denomination, the Strict Baptists, of which only about 150 churches in the UK survive.

From the Metropolitan Tabernacle to the rented room, the trail leads to Chapeltown, another cryptic clue. Chapel towns great and small – thanks.

T.C.

About You

In this book, you, the reader, play the role of one of the detectives in the Quicksolve Detective Agency.

The Quicksolve team are thrilled with their earlier successes in the mysteries of *Sudden Death at the Vicarage*, *The Writing on the Wall* and *The Stolen Statue*. Were you in on those cases? Imagine you and the rest of the team are putting the files from the earlier cases away and looking forward to a few days off when the Boss walks into the office. He has a dreadful grin on his face.

'Nearly finished?' the Boss says, and somehow you know your long weekend is vanishing rapidly. 'Well, I'm sure you'll enjoy sorting out a nice little case we've been sent that's completely baffled the police,' he continues.

'But, er,' you stammer, 'it's the weekend, er, Saturday, Sunday. You know – time off?' But the Boss only chuckles.

'Well, let's put it this way,' he says, 'you'll still be able to go to church.'

'What do you mean?'

'A minister's disappeared, right in front of the very eyes of the congregation.'

'What, during a service?'

'Wow, a deduction like that proves you've got an IQ of at least 75! Yes, she vanished in front of their very eyes.'

Despite looking forward to your weekend, you can't help being interested in this case. 'She?' you ask. 'I assumed ... '

'Well you assumed wrong. He's a she!'

'But if she's been kidnapped, aren't the police ...'

'They were, but they've reached the conclusion that she staged a dramatic walk-out and planned her own disappearance. They've decided it's a "domestic" matter and stopped investigating. They think she walked out on her husband.'

'Was he there at the time?'

'Apparently he wasn't, which is what makes our client wonder if the police have got it wrong.'

'And did the minister walk out on her husband?'

'That's not what our client thinks – she's the minister's best friend, by the way. She's convinced it's a real kidnapping.'

'Sounds fascinating. I'd like to start on this straight away.' You're aware that the Boss is laughing, a deep gurgly laugh like bath-water going down the plug-hole.

'I thought you were on a long weekend?'

'This won't take long,' you reply bravely and walk out before a smart answer can come in reply.

How You Play Detective

In this investigation you will need to work out:

• who is responsible for the minister's disappearance,
• the reason for her disappearance,
• where she is now.

On the evidence you have so far, you can't even be sure a crime has been committed. But if you can find all three answers correctly you will have solved the case, crime or no crime. It is possible that the police have already produced the correct answer. You can't rule that out, at least not yet.

Every few pages in this book, you are asked to choose what you, the detective, do next. When you have decided which clue to follow up or what action to take, you go to another page and read on. But, as in real-life detection, you are working against time. There are several ways of reaching the correct solution to the case, but some take longer than others. Sometimes you will have to decide whether to spend time on extra clues, or whether to manage without. Some choices take longer and tell you in advance to 'add 1 hour to your time score'. When you turn to some other pages, you may find that a choice you have made loses you an hour or more when you weren't expecting it to. This too is like real life because some things take longer than we expect – but the hour must be added to your time score. It is important to write down all these extra hours so that you can keep track of your time score. They are not real hours that you have to add on to reach the solution!

Your time score starts at zero at the beginning of the case. At the very end of the book you will work out a final score based on how much of the solution you got right as well as how long it took you, i.e. the size of your time score. If you use extra clues that add to your time spent, you may be much more likely to get the right solution. If you don't use them, you will be going for a quicker solution, but your chances of getting it wrong may be much higher. It's up to you to weigh up the risks!

You will need a pen or pencil and paper for keeping a note of your time score. It might be useful to have a pad handy to jot down names of suspects, or details of the crime. As you near the end of the book, you may want to write down your deductions –

3

or guesses – about the solution before you actually go on to check it. It's also a good idea to have something you can use as a bookmark so that you don't lose your place, especially if you have to jump to another page to read a clue then back again to where you came from.

The missing person is a Christian minister, so having a Bible handy may help you in your investigation. A few Bible passages are quoted in this book, but you may be able to avoid adding extra hours to your time score by looking them up in a Bible yourself instead.

Now read on. Good luck with the case! Quicksolve are relying on you.

You begin your investigation

Before you set off on the case, you go into your own office to see if there is any more information. The missing minister is a Baptist and her church is in neighbouring Chapeltown. You check exactly where it is by using the street map.

You have to decide immediately what to do next:

- You could drive straight down to the church to see what's been going on. If you want to do this, go to page 5.

- You could call at the library on the way and see what you can find out about Baptists. If you choose to do this, you will have to **add 1 hour to your time score,** but it might give you some background information that will come in handy later in the case. If you want to visit the library, go to page 10. Before you go to page 10, **bookmark this page** in case you need to return to it afterwards.

4

Armed with your map and your client's name and address, you set off for Chapeltown. You find the Baptist church without difficulty and you notice the notice-board immediately:

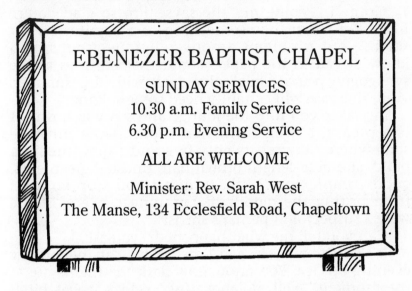

EBENEZER BAPTIST CHAPEL

SUNDAY SERVICES
10.30 a.m. Family Service
6.30 p.m. Evening Service

ALL ARE WELCOME

Minister: Rev. Sarah West
The Manse, 134 Ecclesfield Road, Chapeltown

You walk up the short drive to the door and try it. It is locked. At ground level you notice that there is a foundation stone set into the wall.

Ebenezer Baptist Chapel
Opened 24 March 1887
Stone laid by
Obadiah Watson
Senior Deacon

It might have been open then, but it's closed now! You decide it's time to meet your client, so you look at the address: 132 Ecclesfield Road. That's the street you're in now, and you walk down looking at the numbers until you reach number 132. You ring the bell and produce your Quicksolve identity card, hoping that somebody will be at home. The bell is answered.

'Anna Jackson?' you ask, showing your card.

'Come in, come in,' she says, 'I'm so glad you're here. Your firm has something of a reputation for sorting out problems among religious groups, you know. I read in the papers about that business at the synagogue you at Quicksolve dealt with this summer. Well, this case will certainly need some solving.'

She takes you into the lounge and sits you down. It is a pleasant, well-furnished room. Anna must be somewhere between twenty-five and thirty, medium build, shoulder-length brown hair, unusual green eyes, good complexion. With an effort you stop yourself from noting the details of her appearance as if she were a suspect. But perhaps she is!

'Can you tell me what happened?' you ask.

'It was three weeks ago,' she begins, 'at the Sunday evening service. You know how dark the nights are at the moment. Well, by about five o'clock it was pitch dark outside. We're a growing church – especially since Sarah's been the minister – so although it was a dark winter's night, the service was about half full ...'

'Is that good?' you interrupt.

'Not by morning standards. We're about 80% full then, with lots of families with children, and on special Sundays like Easter it's standing room only. But the evening congregation is smaller, and the average age is older. Families are putting small children to bed or getting ready for work on Monday. One parent might come, whereas in the morning the whole family turns up.'

'Were you there?'

She laughs. 'I'm always there. I'm one of the deacons. I'll explain that later if you want, but I'm there and I usually sit two rows from the front.'

'So you had a good view of what happened?'

'Yes – well, no actually.'

'How do you mean?'

'No-one saw what happened.'

'But you said yourself the church was half full.'

She laughs again. 'Let me finish explaining. In the evening we have a fairly traditional hymn-sandwich service. The minister comes in, reads a line or two from the Bible and announces the first hymn. Then she leads a prayer and we all join in saying the Lord's Prayer, then we sing another hymn. Next follows an Old Testament reading, church notices and the offertory – the weekly collection of money to pay the costs of running the church. After that comes a third hymn, then a New Testament reading, then prayers for people in need, then another hymn – you can see why we nickname it a hymn-sandwich service. Next there's the sermon and another hymn, followed by prayers of dismissal. It's a simple form of service. We like it.

'In the morning we do more varied things. There's a drama group and a music group with keyboards and percussion who accompany some of the songs. Members of the congregation lead different parts of the service. Sometimes we use slides or video ...'

'But in the evening the minister is at the front of the church, alone?'

'Yes, unless it's a Communion service, which this wasn't. We only have Communion in the evening once a month, plus once in a morning service. The minister leads most of the evening service herself, except that I or one of the other deacons reads out the notices.'

'So what happened?'

'It was all perfectly normal until the last verse of the hymn before the sermon. The minister had gone into the pulpit to get ready to preach when the hymn was over, as usual. Then suddenly in the last verse the lights went out. Of course we couldn't see a thing. It was pitch dark. The organ stopped, because it's powered by electricity. You couldn't even see the hymn-book in front of you.'

'Did people panic?'

'Good gracious, no! They all laughed. Everyone assumed it was a power cut, or even a joke, especially since at the time we were singing a famous hymn that starts "Lead, kindly light, amid the encircling gloom"! But when the lights came on, Sarah – our minister – had disappeared. The pulpit was empty. She was nowhere to be seen.'

'How long were the lights off?'

'The police kept asking me that. The fact is, it's very hard even to guess. You couldn't see a watch or anything. It seemed a long time, but then it would, wouldn't it? Perhaps three or four minutes.'

'Did you hear anything during this time?'

'Not a thing. Well, nothing like a scream or a shout if that's what you mean. Just people laughing and talking to the people around them and waiting for the lights to come on.'

'Were the lights off long enough for Sarah to have walked out of the pulpit and out of the building?'

'I think they probably were, and the police assumed that she did just that. In fact, at the time so did we. We thought either she must have gone to sort the fuse out, or else it was some sort of practical joke. But I don't know how she would have seen to walk all down the aisle and out through the entrance porch or into the vestry (that's the minister's office) and out through the back door.'

'Was her husband there? What did he think?'

'No. He doesn't come on Sunday night. He baths the children and puts them to bed and gets ready for work the next morning, so he wasn't there.'

'Mmm.' Anna has given you a lot to think about.

You must decide:

- Whether to go to the library, if you haven't already been there, and find out more about Baptists. If you choose to do this, you will have to **add 1 hour to your time score**, but it might give you a clue that will help to solve the case. If you want to visit the library, go to page 10. Before you go to page 10, **bookmark this page** in case you need to return to it afterwards.

- Whether to question Anna further about Sarah's husband. He might be the key to this mystery. To do this, go to page 19.

- Whether to ask Anna to arrange for the church to be unlocked so that you can inspect for yourself the scene of the disappearance. To do this, go to page 13.

You visit the library

Add 1 hour to your time score.

Here is the information you start piecing together from books in the Christianity section:

Baptists are a world-wide group of Christians, numbering in total about 13 million. So all Baptists are Christians but not all Christians are Baptists. Baptists are like most other Christians in most of their main beliefs, but there is one important difference between Baptists and many (but not all) Christians. This is their view that only believers should be baptized: that is, people who have carefully decided for themselves to become Christians and wish to be baptized into the Christian community. Baptists never baptize babies.

The baptism of a believer is a special event, for that person and for all the people who make up the Baptist church. A special baptism service is held, usually at one of the Sunday service times. After the person has 'testified' or spoken in public during the service about their faith in Jesus, they are baptized, often in a special pool set into the floor of the church. Baptism is by total immersion – in other words, the person is held completely under the water for a few seconds. The symbolic meaning of this is death to their old life (by drowning) and rising, made clean and pure, to their new life in Jesus as a Christian.

John Smyth, one of the founders of the Baptist movement, started to baptize people in this way in Amsterdam in 1609 and a Baptist group began in London in 1612. Smyth believed that he was bringing back the New Testament custom of baptism by doing this. He held that the New Testament talks about the baptism only of adult believers, not of children or babies. Not everyone agreed with him!

Perhaps the most famous of the early British Baptists was John Bunyan (1628 –1688). He was imprisoned in Bedford Gaol for his faith on several occasions and wrote various books, the most famous of which is still in print, *The Pilgrim's Progress* (1678, with a sequel in 1684). This book in turn inspired a Christian hymn which is still widely sung, occasionally in schools as well as churches: 'Who would true valour see', or sometimes with a different first line, 'He who would valiant be'.

10

You think you've heard this hymn and stand in the library trying to hum the words in the reference book you're holding:

Who would true valour see,
Let him come hither;
One here will constant be,
Come wind, come weather;
There's no discouragement
Shall make him once relent
His first avowed intent
To be a pilgrim.

But the glares of other readers while you're humming make you bury your head in the books again and you discover more about Baptists:

Every Baptist church runs itself. It's independent from the others. No Baptist church councils or bishops or Pope exist to tell Baptists what to do. They see themselves as a Christian family gathered together believing that Jesus Christ is the head of the church. Church meetings are held which each member of the church can attend, speak at and vote at. These members are listed on a 'roll', a sort of register which records when people join the church and when they move away or die. The church meetings plan special events, socials and services, raise money for the church and for charities, choose a minister when there is a vacancy, and generally take the decisions for the church. Ministers are not held to be 'in charge' of the other members but are 'first among equals', people trained and working for the church full time. Sometimes they are known as pastors, from a word for 'shepherd', someone having the care of a flock, in this case a flock of people! Every Baptist is a full-time Christian, but most can be only part-time church workers because they have other jobs.

Most Baptist churches don't act alone, however, even though they are independent. Most have chosen to join one of the Baptist Unions which exist to give support and advice (but not commands!) to individual churches. The Baptist Union of Great Britain had 1967 member churches in 1993. It had 148 911 individual members, 2300 ministers, 1031 lay preachers (people who aren't ministers, but who lead services) and 134 791 children and young people. In the smaller Baptist Union of Wales in 1993, there were 544 churches, 25 384 members, 178 ministers, 74 lay preachers and an undeclared total of young people! But thousands of people attend Baptist services without actually being members of the church. Anyone is welcome. Baptist churches aren't members-only secret societies!

The library book you're using goes on to describe much bigger Baptist groups in the southern USA. Here the famous black civil-rights campaigner Dr Martin Luther King (1929–1968) was minister of Dexter Avenue Baptist Church, Montgomery. You read about other big Baptist groups who faced Communist persecution in the old USSR ... but you decide to leave the library because of lack of time and get back on the case.

Go back to the page you came from and choose another route. What you have discovered may be very useful to you as the case develops.

- If you came straight here at the beginning of the investigation, return to page 4.
- If you came here from Anna's house, return to page 9.
- If you came here from the church but have not asked Anna to open the baptistry, return to page 17.
- If you came here after checking up on Sarah, return to page 23.
- If you came here after examining the baptistry, return to page 31.

You inspect the church

Anna has a key to the church and comes down to unlock it for you. You walk in and decide you ought to make a sketch of the ground plan. You know you have to work out how the missing minister left the building during the black-out. But first you look round and try to take it all in.

The building looks very plain. Anna seems to read your thoughts and says:

'Wondering where the crosses and candles and statues and pictures have gone?' You nod.

'We never had them,' she tells you. 'In the early days of our churches it was thought that they might put people off worship, that people would be staring round the building instead of thinking about God. Some people thought that because the Bible doesn't talk about using these objects in worship, we shouldn't have them in churches. Others said that statues would actually break one of the Ten Commandments: the one that says we are not to make images. There were even arguments 150 years ago about whether Baptist churches should have organs, because they aren't mentioned in the Bible either.'

'Not invented then, I suppose?'

'Not in Bible times,' she laughs, 'but we don't treat things that strictly now. If we did, we wouldn't use cars or fridges or microwaves! We'd have to join the Amish! Instead, we've got the latest high-tech digital organ over there.' She points to one side of the building. But you are looking at the pulpit.

'It's massive. You could put half a dozen preachers in there.'

'It's old fashioned! In new churches they're much smaller and often at ground level. But it was built like this because to us the sermon is the central part of the service, the most important bit. We believe that God can use the preacher to speak his message for us. So putting big pulpits in is simply a way of showing how important preaching is.'

'I see you've a big Bible. Is the reason for that the same?'

'Yes, I suppose. It's on the pulpit like that as a sort of symbol that it is at the centre of our faith. Some churches place a Bible open on the Communion table for the same reason.'

'Communion table?'

'Yes, it's not a carved stone altar, like some old parish churches have, or even a decorated wooden table, just a plain one like that,' she points, 'tucked in nt of the pulpit. We put a vase of flowers on it for .ecoration, but it's simple, like the rest of the chapel. Also, Jesus would have eaten his Last Supper at an ordinary table. He made his sacrifice on the Cross, not an altar like the one the Jewish Temple had in those days for killing animals. Neither the Temple nor the animal sacrifices have survived, of course! We use the Communion table as somewhere to stand the bread and wine that are used in the Communion service, the service when we remember Jesus' last meal with his friends.'

You look around. It's logical – a plain building to reflect plain beliefs. Comfortable seats have replaced the old pews or benches since it was built. The simple table, the pulpit, the hymn-board with the numbers of the hymns for the service on ... You try to think about an evening service. No choir. No candles. No complicated symbols. Of course! You remember the minister.

'What was Sarah wearing when she disappeared? A dog-collar? A cloak?'

Anna laughs. 'Some of our ministers wear dog-collars. A few wear what you might call cloaks. We call them gowns. They're plain and black like school-teachers wear in cartoons. But most ministers wear ordinary clothes. It shows they're human like us! We believe that all believers are equal but some are called to serve the church full-time, to minister. That's what "minister" means, to serve.'

'So Sarah was wearing ordinary clothes?'

'Not old jeans and a tee-shirt, if that's what you mean, but a smart dress. She'd have been easy to trace if she'd been all dressed up in a special uniform. But we don't bother with that here.'

15

You decide the time has come to sketch a plan of the building:

You look carefully at what you've drawn, then carefully round the church again. You notice two lots of two steps going down at the front of the church and to the left of the pulpit. But they don't lead anywhere, only to a rectangular area covered with the same sort of carpet as the rest of the floor.

'What are those for?' you ask.

'Oh, it's the baptistry,' says Anna.

'What do you mean?'

'When we have a baptism we never use one of those wooden or stone sinks called fonts you might have seen in other churches. Some of our churches use the river or even the sea, if they're near enough, because the River Jordan was used in Bible times. But most have a baptistry. The steps lead down into a tank, like a sunken bath only deeper, or a mini swimming-pool perhaps! Anyway it's filled with water. The minister goes down into it with the person who's going to be baptized, and everyone can see.'

'So there's a pool under there?'

'Yes, there are two trap-doors covering it now, but when we have a baptism, we open them, of course.'

'How often is that?'

'As often as we have people to be baptized. Three or four times a year on average. Quite often several people are baptized at the same service.'

'Mmm.'

You must decide:

• Whether to find out more about Sarah, the missing minister, if you haven't checked up on her already. To do this, go to page 22.

• Whether to stay here and ask Anna to open the baptistry so that you can look inside it. To do this, go to page 28.

• Whether you need to find out more about Baptists, if you haven't already done so, by visiting the library. If you choose to do this, you will have to **add 1 hour to your time score.** But can you solve the case without this detailed knowledge? If you want to visit the library, go to page 10. Before you go to page 10, **bookmark this page** so that you can return to it afterwards.

• Whether to follow up Anna's strange remark 'We'd have to join the Amish.' Who are they? A gang like the Mafia, perhaps? If you choose to follow up this remark, you will have to **add 1 hour to your time score.** If you still want to do this, go to page 18.

You follow up the strange remark about the Amish

Add 1 hour to your time score.

This is what you find out from reference books in the library:

The Amish are a Baptist group who started in Switzerland in 1693 and now mostly live in the USA. They are strict pacifists and avoid all violence. They refuse to fight in time of war, and in the USA refuse to accept 'the draft', call-up to military service.

They try not to use anything that isn't in the Bible: no buttons on their clothes, no televisions, no freezers, fridges, central heating or cars. Their farms are ploughed by oxen or horses and they use only 'natural' products. They're trying to live what they see as a pure, simple, Bible-based life.

The Amish wouldn't be involved in kidnapping — apart from being wrong, it's violent! Anna obviously mentioned them just as an example of how much more strictly some Christians try to live by the Bible.

This hasn't helped your investigation, except to eliminate the Amish.

Return to page 17 and make another choice.

You question Anna about Sarah's husband

'You said that the police think Sarah walked out on her husband?'

'That's right.'

'But he wasn't there at the time?'

'Exactly.'

'Tell me about him – about them.'

'Well, Sarah met him while she was at university studying Theology – religion, you know. Kevin was studying Mechanical Engineering. He wasn't a Christian then. Not a church-going Christian. He went to a carol service once a year, that sort of thing. For the rest of the year he didn't think about religion much, but he started going to church with her. He was baptized in his last year as a student. After university he worked for various manufacturing companies and now he has his own business, Luxury Lifts Limited. The firm designs, builds and repairs lifts. There's one partner, Bill Foster, though he doesn't live round here. I've never met him. Sarah and Kevin have three small children: Adam, Rachel and Daniel ...'

'Aren't those all Bible names?'

'Yes, that's because we think the Bible is at the heart of Christian belief. Of course it's not more important than Jesus, but it is very important as a record of him and of God's dealings with the Jews. So our children are sometimes named after Bible people and our churches sometimes get called after Bible places, not saints as Church of England or Roman Catholic churches often are. Our church in Chapeltown is called Ebenezer. Everybody used to know what that meant.'

'I'm sorry, er ...'

19

'Don't be. I had to look it up. Ebenezer means something like Stone of Help. It was a place where the Old Testament prophet Samuel set up a memorial stone to remember God's help to the Israelites, more than a thousand years before the Christian era. But other Bible names have been used for churches: Mount Tabor, Bethel, Bethesda, Salem, Zion, Tabernacle. There's even one called Cave Adullam, after the place where David (of David and Goliath fame) hid when he was on the run from King Saul. Otherwise we use plain names like Central Church or name the church after the street it's in. Martin Luther King was minister at Dexter Avenue Church, for instance. Then at Bedford there's the Bunyan Meeting ...'

'Never mind Bunyan! What about Kevin?'

'Oh, yes, Kevin. He and Sarah seem to get on well enough. He's had a lot of business worries recently. Sarah told me privately the firm's having problems financially, so he's been out a lot trying to keep the business going. But she's devoted to him. She wouldn't stage this sort of walk-out on him. Besides, there are the children to think about, and she loves the work here in the church.'

'But the marriage could be under stress, if Kevin's business is in trouble and she's working hard all day for the church.'

'It could be. She has to work a lot of evenings at committees or church meetings or visiting church people who're at work in the day. If you're at work all day, the minister has to extend her working day to see you in the evening or on Saturday. But if the marriage is in a mess, Sarah's never breathed a word. Not a word. And I do know her well. We're good friends, not just deacon and minister. I think she'd tell me if anything was wrong. It's just not like her to bolt. Lots of people can be stressed without running away.'

'Mmm.' You need to think carefully about all this.

At this point you need to decide:

- Whether to inspect the inside of the church and see what you can find out. To do this, go to page 13.

- Whether to add to this information about Kevin by checking up further on Sarah, the missing minister, and finding out more about her life. To do this, go to page 22.

21

You check up on Sarah

You pop back to the Quicksolve office to find that your assistant has gone home. However, there is a brief note waiting for you:

CHECK ON SARAH WEST

BA Theology. Went to Spurgeon's. Spent next three years as assistant minister at a central Baptist church. Then, three years ago, came as minister to Ebenezer, Chapeltown.

She is currently the chairperson for the local branch of Christians Together, a national organization which nearly all the churches in Chapeltown belong to: Roman Catholic, Church of England, Methodist, Baptist, United Reformed. They arrange social events, discussion groups, shared services, the local Christmas-for-the-homeless arrangements, Christian Aid door-to-door collections, and any other activity that churches feel they'll do better together than separately.

Sarah is also one of the chaplains to the local hospital on a part-time basis. She visits patients, is available to talk to worried relatives and holds services there for patients and staff of the hospital. That takes up between one and two days each week. She has a day off (Monday). The rest of the time is spent working for her own church, planning and leading services, visiting members of the congregation, chairing the deacons' meeting, etc.

More than one person has remarked that 'lots of ministers go to Spurgeon's but I don't quite know what to make of this. Didn't think to ask!

Of course, your assistant was keener to start the weekend than you were, so the enquiry's been rather rushed. Spurgeon's. Sounds fishy. Could this be a clue to where Sarah's been taken? Or might there be people there who could throw light on Sarah and her vanishing? If lots of ministers go there, it could give you a vital clue. Perhaps you'd better find this Spurgeon and ask a few questions about Sarah West. As you are pondering what to do, the phone on your desk rings. It's your assistant, who breathlessly blurts out,

'I've found out more. You ought to know this straight away: Spurgeon's dead! That's all I know at the moment, but you can talk to the area superintendent about him.'

You have to decide what to do next:

- You could investigate this Spurgeon and how he fits in, by going to page 24.

- You could inspect the inside of the church, if you haven't already done so, by going to page 13.

- If you have already been into the church, you could ask Anna to open the baptistry for you, by going to page 28.

- You could find out more about Baptists, if you haven't already done so, by visiting the library on page 10 before it closes for the weekend. If you decide to do this, you will have to **add 1 hour to your time score**, but are you out of your depth without more background information? It might provide the clue you need. Before you go to page 10, **bookmark this page** so that you can return to it afterwards.

23

You investigate Spurgeon

The area superintendent is called Fred Humphries. (All Baptists evidently don't have Bible names, you think to yourself. At least, there are no Freds you've heard of in the Bible!) He's an experienced minister, who looks after his own church, but he's available as a friend and support to other ministers in the area. He isn't their boss, he's an equal and an adviser they can turn to if needed. That's what the area superintendent does.

'Terrible business, this,' he says to you as he sits back in the book-lined study in his manse or clergy house. 'Poor Sarah, I hope you get to the bottom of it.'

'I certainly hope I can,' you reply. 'In fact I hope you can throw some light on the case quickly, because one of the people involved is dead.'

'Dead? Then things are getting sinister. Who? How?'

'I was rather hoping you could tell me. I'm talking about Spurgeon.'

Fred Humphries sits bolt upright in his chair. His face registers absolute surprise and disbelief. He stares at you, saying nothing. You wonder what he's holding back. When he does speak, it is only to repeat what you've said:

'Spurgeon? You said Spurgeon?'

'That's right.'

'Charles Haddon Spurgeon?'

'I don't know his or her forenames, but I expect you're right if he's the one lots of ministers go to.' Then the unpredictable happens. Fred Humphries throws back his head and roars with laughter, on and on, until he starts coughing, tears streaming down his face. You're rather annoyed about all this.

'I don't see that this is any laughing matter,' you begin.

24

'Oh it is, it is, I assure you,' he manages to choke out between laughter and coughing.

'Well, would you mind letting me in on the secret?'

'No secret, no secret. Public knowledge,' he gets his breath back and calms down, 'Charles Haddon Spurgeon's been dead since 1892.'

'1892? Then how can lots of minister go to see him? There must be someone else.'

'No, it's him all right. You see, Charles Haddon Spurgeon was probably the most successful British Baptist preacher of all time. I even know some of his dates by heart as I had to study him as part of my course at college. He was born in 1834, became a Baptist in 1850 and minister of a church at Waterbeach in Cambridgeshire at the very young age, even for those days, of seventeen. His fame as a preacher quickly spread and a London church quickly snapped him up to be their minister at New Park Street Chapel. He was then only twenty.

'The chapel filled so quickly that they decided to rent the Surrey Gardens Music Hall to fit all the people in. This went on for three years and he preached to weekly congregations of more than ten thousand. Think of that – ten thousand! People had to queue to get a seat. In the end a new massive church, the Metropolitan Tabernacle, near London's Elephant and Castle, had to be built for him.

'While all this was going on his sermons were being published and posted world-wide every week. They're still in print, along with his more everyday articles under the pen-name, John Ploughman. His words were printed in magazines as well, like *Sword and Trowel*. That's still issued, by the way, so millions read him who never heard him.'

'What was his secret?' you ask.

'To look at he was podgy, rather unimpressive, but he was a man of prayer and a no-nonsense minister.

He wouldn't wear clerical clothes – minister's uniform – or take the title Reverend, and he spoke in ordinary language, not posh, with a sense of humour. His sermons lasted for well over an hour, sometimes two. What would modern church-goers make of them?!

'Sadly, he died of illness brought on by overwork in 1892. They put a Bible quote on his coffin: "I have fought a good fight, I have finished my course, I have kept the faith." His pulpit Bible from the Tabernacle was placed on the coffin. London was completely blocked by the horse-drawn funeral traffic and a hundred thousand people turned up. In his time as Tabernacle minister nearly fifteen thousand people were recorded attending the church and there were more than eight thousand children in his various Sunday schools.'

'But how can ministers go to Spurgeon's now?'

'Simple. He established a pastors' college to train new ministers. Many young men and women have gone there over the years to study for the ministry: Spurgeon's College, known for short as Spurgeon's. Sarah went to Spurgeon's, but that doesn't help your enquiry. By the way, Spurgeon also set up what in those days was called an orphanage. It still exists as a child-care charity.'

So it's all been a red-herring. Spurgeon is dead, but he's been dead for more than a century. Taking your leave of Fred, you feel embarrassed. You think of a few well-chosen words for your assistant when you meet on Monday morning.

Meanwhile this conversation has taken time:

Add 1 hour to your time score.

Return to page 23 and make another choice.

27

You ask Anna to open the baptistry

'It might be a bit dusty, because it's not been used for about three months,' she laughs, pulling away the carpet covering. The dust rises and makes you cough. The carpet reveals two long doors neatly set into the floor, with bolts as well as handles.

'Could you give me a hand?' asks Anna, and you each take one of the handles and pull back the two trap-doors. They open upwards. You peer in.

The two steps at each end that you can see when the doors are closed continue downwards, with five more on each side, into a rectangular, white-tiled pool. A tall person standing in it might have their head and shoulders above the floor level of the church building. There are two taps on one of the long walls and there is a drain plug on the floor, which slopes very gently towards the plug end.

'What happens when ...?' you start to ask.

'Most of the service happens before the baptism: hymns, songs, readings, prayers, a sermon. The sermon nearly always tries to help the person (or people) about to be baptized to think about how serious and how super baptism is as the gateway to Christian life. It also reminds those who've already been baptized what it should mean for them. The person being baptized sometimes gives a short testimony – a talk, sort of report – about what has led them to do this and how they see it as God's wish for them.

'At the point of the service of the actual baptism the person comes down into the water, which is just above waist high, with the minister. In most churches they lend you a baptismal gown to wear over your clothes. Sometimes it's a long white robe. We do that here. The ministers in some churches wear anglers' waders to keep their clothes dry, but again here our minister wears ordinary clothes and a white gown over them. The water's warm, by the way, so you don't take an icy plunge!

'The minister holds you carefully and says, "We baptize you in the name of God the Father, Son and Holy Spirit", or "In the name of Christ" – there's no set wording. They then lower you backwards, cradled in their arms, right under the water for a few seconds, then bring you up again. This symbolizes dying to your old life and starting a new life in Jesus. It's very public and very personal at the same time. Sometimes people come up laughing or crying, not because of the water, but because it's the most memorable moment of their religious life up to that point. Then they walk up out of the baptistry and get changed in a room at the back while one of the deacons leads the service and the congregation sing a hymn. The now-dry minister and the newly baptized Christian arrive back in time for the end of the service.'

'When did you say the last baptism here was?'

'About three months ago.' You walk down into the dry baptistry and look around. Along one of the tiled walls there are cracks running along the line of the tile cement, near the floor.

'I wonder, could you try to fill the baptistry, because it looks cracked to me?' you ask. Anna looks surprised.

'Well, it was perfectly all right last time we had a baptism. Still, if you really want to see.' She turns the taps on. You come up the steps so as not to get wet. The water is pouring in from the two taps. But although the pool does start to fill, it is obvious that there's a water loss through the two vertical cracks you spotted. Anna turns the taps off quickly.

'I can't keep running the water, because it will get into the surrounding ground and cause damp under the church floor. We're obviously going to have to get that leak fixed before the next baptism service.

30

Otherwise they'll be only ankle deep. Imagine trying to immerse people under three inches of water!

'We've been wondering whether to replace this pool with a modern fibreglass one,' she explains. 'Maybe this leak will help us decide.'

You help Anna to drain the baptistry and replace first the trap-doors, then the carpet. As you do this, you try to work out what this might mean.

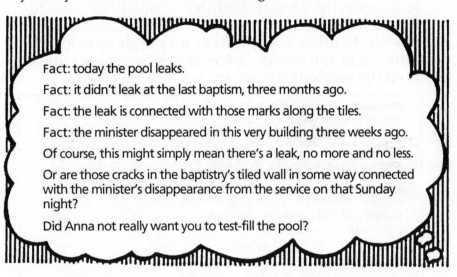

Fact: today the pool leaks.

Fact: it didn't leak at the last baptism, three months ago.

Fact: the leak is connected with those marks along the tiles.

Fact: the minister disappeared in this very building three weeks ago.

Of course, this might simply mean there's a leak, no more and no less.

Or are those cracks in the baptistry's tiled wall in some way connected with the minister's disappearance from the service on that Sunday night?

Did Anna not really want you to test-fill the pool?

You must choose:

• Whether the time has come to talk to Kevin, Sarah's husband, by going to page 35.

• Whether to continue your search of the church and see if anything else looks odd, by going to page 32.

• Whether to find out more about Baptists, if you haven't already done so, before you get out of your depth in this pool, by going to the library on page 10. If you decide to do this, you will have to **add 1 hour to your time score**, but it may give you the background you need. Before you go to page 10, **bookmark this page** so that you can return to it afterwards.

You continue your search of the church

In such a plain building, there isn't a lot to check. You wander along some of the rows of seats, but they all look perfectly normal. Each has a small ledge on the back and on the ledge are placed a hymn-book and a modern translation of the Bible for people to follow the readings in the service. A few ledges have notice sheets from the previous Sunday service. You look at one.

EBENEZER BAPTIST CHURCH
Pastor: Sarah West
WELCOME TO THIS WEEK'S ACTIVITIES
Sunday
10.30 Family Service, with junior church and crèche
6.30 Evening Service
Preacher at both services: John Ingram (Deacon)
Theme: Alive in God's World
Collections this week: church funds + special collection (evening) for Christian Aid

Monday
2.30 Women's Group
7.30 Bible Study Group A

Tuesday
9.30 Pre-school play group
2.30 Senior citizens' afternoon club
7.30 Church music group practice

Wednesday
9.30 Pre-school play group
12.30 Lunch club
7.30 Deacons' meeting

Thursday
9.30 Pre-school play group
12.30 Munch 'n' pray short lunchtime service
7.30 Church drama group practice

Friday
9.30 Bible study group B
6.30 Young youth club (7s to 12s)
8.00 Elderly youth club (13+)

You decide to keep a copy of this sheet in case it's of any use later. You walk up to the Communion table and examine it. It's a plain wooden table. No drawers. No cloth covering it. There's a row of chairs behind it, below the pulpit.

'That's where the minister and deacons sit at Communion,' explains Anna. 'The bread is taken round by us to the people. They stay in their seats. The same with the wine.'

'I thought it was in a big cup, a goblet, you all shared.'

'In lots of churches it is, in what they call a chalice, but Baptists prefer small individual glasses. That means everyone can take Communion – eat the bread then drink the wine – at exactly the same time. After all, the Last Supper was a shared meal. Jesus and the disciples ate and drank together and we're trying to model our Communion service on that.'

'So it's really in memory of him and that last meal?'

'Absolutely! But it also reminds us of our belief that he's alive and present with us now.'

'Only baptized believers can take Communion, then?'

'Not at all. Any person who, in words we often use at the service, "loves the Lord Jesus" can take Communion. We don't mind whether they've been baptized by immersion as believers or whether they belong to some other church or whether they're not official members of any church. If they want to share in the Lord's Supper, he welcomes them. It's not up to us to make rules to keep people out. It's his meal, not ours, that we share together ...'

While she's been explaining this, you've wandered up into the pulpit. You certainly get a good view from up here. On the pulpit desk top are the large Bible, a hymn-book, and plenty of room for the notes of the person leading the service. Behind is a seat, so that you could sit during the singing of a hymn. Anna guesses your thoughts.

'We don't kneel for prayers here,' she says, 'mostly we sit. Occasionally we stand.'

'Why don't you kneel?'

'It's partly history. When our churches first started, kneeling was associated with the Roman Catholic and Anglican churches and we didn't want to copy them. Kneeling doesn't seem natural nowadays like it did when you knelt in front of kings and emperors. Of course, we are a Free Church and there's nothing to stop you from kneeling if you want. You wouldn't get thrown out or anything.'

But while she's talking you hear a creaking. You stop pacing up and down in the pulpit. The creaking stops. You walk again. The creaking starts again. You stop. It stops. Anna is watching you, slightly alarmed. The floorboards feel as if they're loose.

What are you going to do? Think about it. Friendly as Anna is, you can't rule her out as a suspect.

- If you want to avoid arousing her suspicions, you could leave now and talk to Sarah's husband, Kevin, if you haven't already done so, by going to page 35.

- Perhaps you can risk her seeing you. If so, you could stay here and find out just what that creaking is, by going to page 43.

- You could play safe and do more fact-finding, this time into what Free Churches are, by going to page 40. You've heard the phrase 'Free Church' before. But if the church is free, surely Sarah wouldn't be kidnapped for money and they wouldn't need those collections for church funds that are listed on the notice sheet?

You talk to Kevin, Sarah's husband

When you arrive at the minister's house or manse, as it is known, you're pleased to find Kevin is at home. He opens the door and you explain who you are. Kevin, not surprisingly, is a worried-looking man, thin-faced, thinning hair, slim, pale. He seems rather distracted and not that anxious to talk.

'I wasn't expecting you,' he explains, 'and coping with my job and the children is keeping me fully occupied – though I'm delighted that someone is working on the case.' But he doesn't look remotely delighted. You follow him into the lounge, which is untidy, and perch on the edge of a settee covered with letters and papers. You notice a newspaper called the *Baptist Times* with a front-page article headed 'MINISTER MISSING'.

'Tell me,' you ask, 'what do you think has happened to Sarah?'

'I wish I knew,' he replies, 'I wish I knew.'

'Was she any different on the Sunday she vanished? Did she behave oddly? Say something unusual? That sort of thing?'

'I've gone over and over it in my mind and nothing seemed out of the ordinary.'

'But you weren't there when it happened?'

'No, I was here, putting the children to bed.'

'If she has been kidnapped, what do you think the reason might be?'

'I thought people were only kidnapped for money.'

'She hasn't got any?'

'I don't know how much you know about ministers, but I can tell you they aren't paid very much. Some

35

don't even earn enough to pay income tax, so no kidnapper's going to get rich on a minister!'

'What was she doing in the days leading up to her disappearance?'

'Have a look at her personal organizer if you like. It's over there.' He points to some papers on the table in the corner of the room. You go across to read the organizer, but you can't help noticing a large pile of bills on the same table. Gas. Water. Electricity. Credit cards. Council tax. You pick up the organizer and find the week before Sarah disappeared.

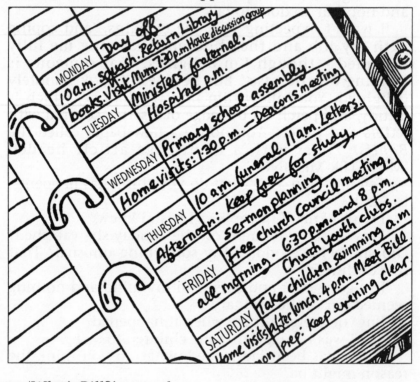

'Who's Bill?' you ask.

'Oh, just a tramp who rolled up at the door asking for food.'

'Do you get many tramps?'

'All the time! Would you like a cup of tea?'

'Yes, please.' Kevin seems to be friendlier now. Perhaps he realizes that he might otherwise appear to be friendlier to the visiting tramps than to you. He goes off to make the tea in the kitchen. You look at the papers scattered over the settee. There are several copies of the *Baptist Times* and you look idly at the headlines.

You continue flicking through the letters and papers. More bills. To your surprise you see betting-slips – receipts from gambling on horse racing. They're for quite large amounts: £25, £50. Aren't they rather unexpected? Among them is a typed letter addressed to Sarah. You note from the postmark that it must have arrived after her disappearance.

You have to make a fast decision. Should you open the letter and read it? Remember that it isn't yours, it's a private letter, and Kevin might come in at any moment. If he comes in while you're reading it there could be a mega row. Perhaps you should ignore it and just wait for Kevin to bring your tea.

- If you want to risk opening the letter, go to page 42.

- If you don't, read on.

You're ready for that cup of tea. While you chat to Kevin about the weather and other trivial things, you're deciding in your own mind what to do next.

You have three choices:

- To find out about Free Churches, because you've seen them mentioned in the personal organizer, by going to page 40.

- To investigate the strange diary entry for Saturday about Bill the tramp, by going to page 48. This is bound to **add 1 hour to your time score**.

- To read the MINISTER MISSING article in the *Baptist Times*, by going to page 38.

You read the MINISTER MISSING article in the *Baptist Times*

You didn't know that Baptists had their own weekly newspaper. You see that its weekly circulation is 11 000, which means that more people than that must read it, because families will share a copy, some people will pass theirs on, etc. You see from its address that it's produced at the headquarters of the Baptist Union of Great Britain, at Didcot in Oxfordshire. You glance at some of the other headlines.

You look at the inside and see an advertisement for glass fibre baptismal pools above a list of recent baptisms. It's a weekly list and tells readers where the baptisms took place and the number of people baptized in each church. You can't resist being a detective here and trying to work out who or what the churches are named after. You find two called after

Baptisms

Andover:	2	Minchinhampton:	7
Barnstaple:	2	Moulton (Carey):	2
Birmingham (Yardley Wood):	1	Penarth (Tabernacle,	
Chiswick:	2	Plassey Street):	3
Cinderford:	3	Pinner (United Free):	1
Colne (Trinity):	1	Slough:	1
Crewe (Union Street):	6	Stevenage (Bunyan):	2
Frinton-on-Sea		Whitstable (Middle Wall):	1
(Connaught Avenue):	5	Total:	53
Haddenham, Cambs:	1		
Ipswich (Rushmere):	1	Total from January 1:	1813
Ipswich (Whitehouse):	1		
London (East Plumstead):	1	Comparative figure	
London (Willesden Green):	7	for last year	2013
Lyme Regis (Silver Street):	3		

38

people, one after something in the Bible (and a street), one after an important Christian belief and three more called after the street they're in.

You return to the front page and skim-read the article about Sarah's disappearance:

MINISTER MISSING

Very popular minister ... growing church ... great mystery ... in the middle of the service ... The police were called ... they withdrew from the case ... No motive for her disappearance ... Kidnapping dismissed as gossip by her husband, a company director ... No ransom demand received ...

Odd, you hadn't thought about that before. No ransom demand has been received, unless Kevin's too frightened to tell the police about it.

Put the paper down and return to page 37 to make another choice.

ulgarian Baptists ace false charges

Bibles in demand in Iraq

You find out about Free Churches

This involves a long series of calls on your car-phone to various ministers to find out what they can tell you. This is the information you gather.

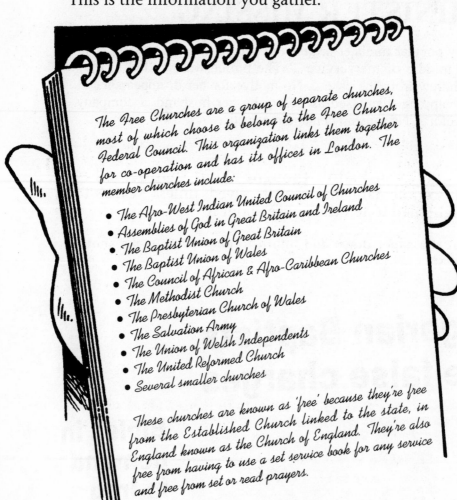

The Free Churches are a group of separate churches, most of which choose to belong to the Free Church Federal Council. This organization links them together for co-operation and has its offices in London. The member churches include:

- The Afro-West Indian United Council of Churches
- Assemblies of God in Great Britain and Ireland
- The Baptist Union of Great Britain
- The Baptist Union of Wales
- The Council of African & Afro-Caribbean Churches
- The Methodist Church
- The Presbyterian Church of Wales
- The Salvation Army
- The Union of Welsh Independents
- The United Reformed Church
- Several smaller churches

These churches are known as 'free' because they're free from the Established Church linked to the state, in England known as the Church of England. They're also free from having to use a set service book for any service and free from set or read prayers.

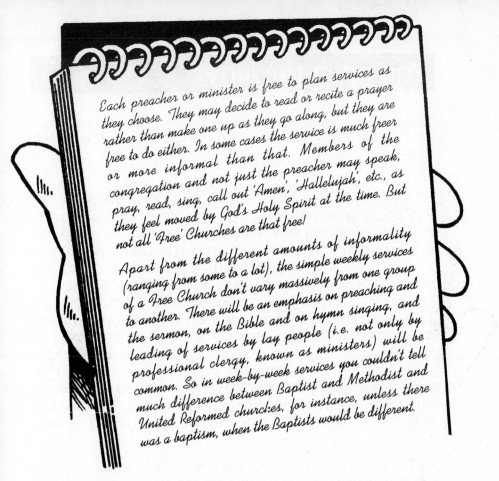

Each preacher or minister is free to plan services as they choose. They may decide to read or recite a prayer rather than make one up as they go along, but they are free to do either. In some cases the service is much freer or more informal than that. Members of the congregation and not just the preacher may speak, pray, read, sing, call out 'Amen', 'Hallelujah', etc., as they feel moved by God's Holy Spirit at the time. But not all 'Free' Churches are that free!

Apart from the different amounts of informality (ranging from some to a lot), the simple weekly services of a Free Church don't vary massively from one group to another. There will be an emphasis on preaching and the sermon, on the Bible and on hymn singing, and leading of services by lay people (i.e. not only by professional clergy, known as ministers) will be common. So in week-by-week services you couldn't tell much difference between Baptist and Methodist and United Reformed churches, for instance, unless there was a baptism, when the Baptists would be different.

This check has taken time.

Add 1 hour to your time score.

You can now either return at once to the page you came from or first check up further on Baptists and Christians, if you're still confused about them.

- To return to your cup of tea with Kevin, go to page 37.

- To return to your search of the church, go to page 34.

- To try to sort out the link between Baptists and Christians, go to page 47. Before you go to page 47, **bookmark this page** so that you can return to it afterwards.

You open the letter

Turn the page upside down to find out what the letter says, then turn it back and follow the instructions at the bottom of the page.

Nosy! It's not a ransom note, just Sarah's bank statement. You read that she has £128 976 in her account. That's a lot of money, and one week ago, according to the date on the statement, £20 000 was withdrawn.

Was this to meet a ransom demand that Kevin hasn't told you about? Or has she walked out and is in hiding somewhere living off this money? Abroad? Where did she get money like that? Could she really be the criminal, posing as the victim?

Quickly you stuff the statement back into its envelope and put it back where you found it. You can hear Kevin crossing the hall. He's almost reached the lounge door.

- If you have just met Kevin for the first time and he left the room to make you a cup of tea, return to page 37.

- If Kevin left the room to answer the door, return to page 58.

42

You investigate the creaking in the pulpit

The strange creaking and the slight rocking of the pulpit floor continue as you walk up and down on it. There's quite a layer of dust on the floor but the vibration seems to be coming from under it. Acting on impulse you start to jump up and down, much to Anna's amazement and amusement. She doesn't seem to know whether to laugh or whether to protest about your rather disrespectful behaviour. Before you can tell her why you're doing it, all at once there's a cracking noise, then a loud crash. It seems as if in a split second you've fallen, banged the back of your head and the lights have gone out. Perhaps you're unconscious? Though if you were unconscious, would you be able to wonder whether you were?

You're certainly rather dazed, because of the fall, and your head aches at the back. One of your ankles has been wrenched and you are in total darkness. Where are you? What's happened? It feels as if you're in some sort of container, a sort of tube. You're upright, because it's much too narrow to lie down in, and you can feel in the dark that the sides of the tube are cold and damp. Whether they're hard earth or concrete or some other substance, you can't tell. It seems that in the distance Anna is shouting and calling your name. She sounds a long way off, but perhaps you're still dizzy from the fall and can't hear her properly.

Although you can't lie down, you discover that you can shuffle down into a kneeling position and from that get onto all fours on the cold floor. You crawl around in a circle and, to your surprise, you find a hole. There's some sort of round tunnel about a metre in diameter that leads out of the bottom of the tube you're trapped in. You decide to crawl along it to see if you can find a way out. Gingerly, feeling carefully in the pitch dark with your hands in front of you, you set off. You are frightened, but you aren't sure why. Is someone or something down there? Spiders or worse? Are you entombed? In fact you haven't gone far before you come to a wall: a dead end.

Now you do feel trapped, because the tunnel is much too narrow to turn round in. You can't go back, except by very slow reversing, shuffling backwards on all fours. Nor can you hear Anna any more. She must have gone. Or been taken. You think hard and try to decide what to do. Perhaps the tunnel has a bend you've missed. You crawl forward again. Bang! It's your forehead this time. Another bruise. Strange, it was a rather hollow bang. You didn't think your head was that empty. Wait a minute! It's not your head, it's the wall! It's not solid at all. You push very hard with both hands in front of you in the darkness. Gradually there's a slow grinding movement and what you thought was the wall swings away on a hinge you can't see.

This time you're in a bigger chamber. Keeping your nerve, you start to feel your way around it in the blackness. The walls are smooth and cold. You find you can stand up, provided you stay in a stooping position. You can walk up and down in the narrow rectangular chamber. When you touch the ceiling, you discover it's wooden, with a ridge down the middle. You knock on it. Definitely wood. You seem to be at one end of a rectangular cellar with steps leading upwards to this ceiling.

Know where you are yet? If you do, you also now hold all the clues as to how the minister disappeared. If you don't understand what happened yet, read through this section again and think carefully about what it might mean. If you're right, you should also know how you can send for help to get out, and exactly how you can escape from this rectangular underground room with the assistance of someone outside.

Only when you're sure you know or if you really can't work out the answer, turn to page 46.

45

The wooden 'roof' is the underside of the trap-doors that lead into the baptistry. You don't have to bang on them for long before you hear the bolts being drawn and they're raised up. Anna has come to your rescue. Once the doors are open, you can walk up the steps and back into the church.

'I've found out how Sarah was kidnapped,' you start to explain, excitedly.

'That's easy,' interrupts Anna. 'When you fell through the floor like an idiot, I stared at the boards and I could clearly see a proper hinged trap. Looks like it was connected to some sort of electrical device: a timer, or a radio control. That would mean that at the exact moment the kidnapper chose, the door could drop Sarah into the hole then re-close, just as it did when you crashed through it. I bet it was linked in some way to the black-out in the service. Whoever did it also scattered thick dust on the pulpit floor to cover up the marks they'd made.'

But Sarah wouldn't have kept quiet down that hole all the time until she could be got out of the building after the service was over, you think to yourself. So there must have been at least two kidnappers involved, one to do the lights and one concealed in the baptistry before the service started, waiting to gag her or whatever ... unless she did stage her own disappearance. But why?

If you're still confused about the link between Baptists and Christians, you can try to sort that out by going to page 47. Could this give you the vital lead you're looking for?

Otherwise:

- If you haven't met Kevin, Sarah's husband, talk to him now by going to page 35.
- If you have met Kevin but not investigated Bill the tramp, do this now by going to page 48.
- If you have already investigated Bill the tramp, you must now check up on Anna by going to page 51.

46

You try to sort out the link between Baptists and Christians

You decide to nip back to the Quicksolve office to consult the encyclopedia. On the way, you go over in your mind what you already know. Let's see ... All Baptists are Christians, but of course not all Christians are Baptists. Some are Methodists or Church of Scotland or Roman Catholics or something else. You can just remember an RE textbook in your schooldays which showed Christian groups like the sections of an orange.

The office encyclopedia tells you that the names of many of these groups grew from nicknames. Even Christians weren't called that in the early years. They were called 'followers of the Way', 'brethren' and other names that didn't stick. In later times 'Methodist' was a nickname given to some Christians because of their methodical, careful approach to prayer and Bible study. They used method! Quakers trembled or quaked in their meetings when they felt moved by God's Holy Spirit to stand up and speak. Baptists thought the baptism of believers (and not babies) was important.

So the name of the religion is Christianity and these other names, including Baptist, describe or denominate different sub-groups, hence their technical name: Christian denominations. But the common denominator shared by all of them is trying to follow Jesus Christ.

Mmm. That seems more or less clear, and it took you less time than you thought it might.

• If you came here from finding out about Free Churches, return to page 41.

• If you came here after investigating the pulpit, return to page 46.

You investigate Bill the tramp

Add 1 hour to your time score.

'Dreadful business, this, about Sarah,' says the vicar of Chapeltown. You've popped in to see him in the hope that he can help with the identity of local tramps.

'I suppose she's a sort of rival of yours, Baptist Church versus Church of England?' you ask.

'Absolutely right – a hundred and fifty years ago,' explains the vicar. 'There were real rivalries then, but not today. Now we think that what Christians agree about matters much more than what we don't.'

'So her church and yours could unite?'

'We do a lot of things together already, and in some places churches have united. The reason for staying separate is in the end, I guess, not that either church thinks we're better than the other. It's just that we have a few differences of belief – about baptism, for instance – and our services are a bit different. So it's partly a matter of people going to the type of service that appeals to them best. But I thought you'd come to talk about tramps not churches?' You nod.

'We get tramps calling all the time. All the time. Did you know that most vicars and ministers do? In our case it's because we're on the main road to Manchester. The tramps walk along it, then walk back towards Derby. Takes them the summer months to do it, sleeping rough. So when they see a vicarage or a manse, they think because we're Christian leaders we'll be an easy touch. In a way we are, because Jesus told his followers to help people so we can't refuse.'

'Do you give them money?'

'Never! Partly because vicars and ministers haven't got much, partly because, well, when I was young and

48

innocent I was conned into giving a tramp forty quid once, and he drank it!'

'What do you do now?'

'Now I give them a good mug of tea – never alcohol, because with some of them that's been the start of their problems. We also make a few good thick cheese sandwiches, or we go to the fish and chip shop and I load them up there with fish, double chips and lots of mushy peas. Course, we've got to know most of them quite well over the years.'

'Bill?'

'No, we don't give them a bill.' He guffaws with laughter at his own joke. You force a polite grin which nearly cracks your jaw.

'I mean, do you know a tramp called Bill?'

'I can't say I do, and I've been a vicar here now for about fourteen years. Bill, no, there's never been a Bill among the tramps I've ever got to know. Hang on a minute while I ask my wife.' He pops out of his study and returns shortly after.

'No, definitely not,' he says. 'My memory for names isn't as good as it was but, er, er, what's her name, she, my wife, says she's quite sure we've had no Bill.' His joke about his wife leads him into explosive laughter. Your eardrums take the strain and you excuse yourself, leaving quickly with a new corny joke about getting

the No Bill Peas Prize ringing in your ears. You wonder if his sermons are packed with jokes like that!

You try to forget the jokes and concentrate on 'Bill'. Could he be part of the solution to this mystery? He's not one of the regular tramps. But he might be a new one Sarah was trying to help. Or was he somehow involved in the kidnapping? You certainly can't rule him out.

You must decide:

- Whether to resume your search of the church if you left it to meet Kevin immediately after Anna showed you the baptistry. To do this, go to page 32.

- Whether to return to the church and investigate the pulpit if that's what you were looking at just before you went to meet Kevin. To do this, go to page 43.

- Whether to investigate Anna. She seems so pleasant and she is Sarah's best friend, but she must be a suspect. To do this, you will have to go back to the Quicksolve office and start ringing round Baptist contacts in Ebenezer and other churches in the area to see what you can discover. This means you will have to **add 1 hour to your time score**, but it may be your only option at this point in the case. To check up on Anna, travel to page 51.

You check up on Anna

Add 1 hour to your time score.

You return to the Quicksolve office, put your favourite CD on the music centre, make a coffee and start dialling round your Baptist contacts. You begin with John Ingram, one of the other deacons named on the church notice sheet.

'Well,' he says, 'Anna's been a deacon as long as me. She comes from a good Christian family and she's a very good friend of Sarah, which is useful for a deacon.'

'What exactly is a deacon?'

'It's a bit confusing, because the name refers to different jobs in different Christian churches. In the Bible, in the book called Acts of the Apostles, the deacons were seven people chosen to be responsible for the day-to-day things in the Christian community: finance, looking after widows (no DSS benefits and pensions then!), that sort of thing. The idea was to free the disciples to get on with preaching, teaching and spreading Christianity.

'In Baptist churches there's a similar set-up. The deacons are responsible for the day-to-day running of the church, including repairs to the building and finance. Our treasurer, William Lord, is a deacon, for example. Deacons should free the minister to get on with preaching, visiting the sick and so on, although the minister chairs the deacons' meetings and works with them closely in practice. Minister and deacons all work hard for the church, but deacons aren't full-time.

'Another thing Sarah and Anna have in common is that they're both involved in the Guild of Baptist Campers.'

'The what?'

51

'Being a Christian – and a Baptist Christian in particular – isn't just about going to church and trying to follow Christ and help others. Baptists often raise money for Christian causes like Christian Aid or the Baptist Housing Association, which provides housing for retired ministers or their widows or widowers, but that isn't all either. With so much in common we enjoy a social life together as well. There are social groups like the Baptist Caravan Fellowship or the Guild of Baptist Campers which get people from different churches together for activities they enjoy, like camping. Sarah and Anna have been on lots of holidays with them. So it's not surprising Anna's not given up and won't accept the police view that Sarah might have walked out ...'

He's still talking but you hold the phone away from your ear and think about it. Anna's the one who has pushed to keep the case open. It couldn't be her, could it? You thank John Ingram and ring off. Almost immediately the phone rings. It's the Boss in person!

'What are you doing in the office?' You turn the CD down, put your mug of coffee in a drawer and close it, as if the Boss can see you!

'I'm making enquiries about one of the deacons.'

'Well don't bother! While you've been messing around back in the office, Anna Jackson – our client – has rung me to say that she's just had a message from Sarah. You'd better get back on the case right away.'

It reminds you of when you were at school. Why did the teachers always look over your shoulder and read the worst bits of your work and not the best?

Drive across to page 53 without delay.

You meet Anna to hear about the message

'She's alive! She's safe!' Anna greets you at the door of her house, waving a sheet of paper. Before you can get in and sit down she gives it to you. The envelope just says 'ANNA' on the outside. She tells you it was pushed through her letter-box sometime in the last couple of hours. You read the letter carefully.

I'm safe. Don't worry.
Tell Kevin. Pray for me.
Bible readings help:
Gen 31:15b, Ps 35:7b
Prov 13:8a, Ps 142:7a,
Ps 71:14a.
No need for private eye. Love Pony.

'We can't be sure she's still alive,' you ponder, 'because we don't know when she wrote this. We don't even know that it's from her. It could be forged.'

'Oh no it's not,' interrupts Anna. 'It's not just her writing. She's used her old childhood nickname, Pony, as a way of identifying herself. I called her that because she was mad about horse riding. It's from her all right.'

That still leaves you with several questions to think about. Why did she not write to her husband? Or has he received a note too? How does she know you're looking for her? She couldn't know Quicksolve are involved unless her kidnapper or kidnappers have told her, so they must know. Why does she not want Quicksolve to be involved? Or has she been told to write that by the kidnapper or kidnappers?

Why has she bothered to fill a short note with what seems to be a list of Bible passages that have helped her? You remember reading that Terry Waite used Bible and prayer-book sentences in his 1763 days of captivity as a hostage in Beirut.

'Sarah must know her Bible very well to be able to remember those quotations and know where they come from,' you observe to Anna.

'Lots of Christians do know their Bible well,' she explains, 'although some hardly know it at all.'

'What do you think "Gen", "Ps" and "Prov" mean?'

'They're abbreviations for books in the Bible,' says Anna, 'Genesis, Psalms and Proverbs.'

'Why should she be reading them?'

'Looks like she's been allowed a Bible by her kidnapper or kidnappers.'

'Isn't it a bit surprising she's not reading the Gospels and other New Testament stories to cheer herself up?'

'I suppose it is.'

'What does 31:15b, 35:7b and all that stuff mean?'

'Well, long after they were written, the books in the Bible were divided into chapters and verses, though the chapters are a lot shorter than chapters in modern books and the verses are not rhymes or poetry, but sentences. This system was intended to make it easier for people to look bits up, even if they were using different translations. Each chapter and verse was given a number, so 31:15b means chapter 31, verse 15b. The "b" means the second half of the verse.'

'So Sarah's given you exact Bible sentences she's been reading?'

'That's right.'

'But she's not listed them in the proper order. Even I can see that. The order must have some meaning ...'

You don't want to give away too many of your thoughts to Anna, just in case she's a suspect. So you thank her, leave and go and sit in your car, taking the note with you.

- If you have a (real) Bible with you, look up the passages listed in Sarah's note and see if they make any sense. Then read on.

- If you don't have a Bible with you, you can read the passages listed in Sarah's note by turning to page 57, but you will have to add **TWO hours to your time score**. So it's well worth trying to find the passages in a (real) Bible if you can. If you do decide to go to page 57, **bookmark this page** first so that you can return to it afterwards.

When you have read the Bible passages, wherever you've found them, you must decide:

- Whether the time has come to try to check how much money Sarah has, by going to page 59. Can you risk spending an hour or more doing this?

- Whether to show Kevin Sarah's note, by going to page 58.

You run outside to try to catch Bill

Turn the page upside down to find out what happens, then turn it back and follow the instructions at the bottom of the page.

The street is empty. Whoever Bill is, he's nowhere in sight. Perhaps he drove off in a car. But if he's a tramp he won't have a car. It doesn't make sense ... does it?

You must decide what to do next:

- You could sit in your own car to think things over, by going to page 63.

- You could try to check how much money Sarah has, if you haven't already done so, by going to page 59.

You need help to look up the Bible passages

You go to a Christian friend's house to borrow his Bible. He's keen to help but keeps you talking and insists that you have a snack before you leave.

Add 2 hours to your time score.

This is what the Bible passages in Sarah's note say:

Genesis 31:15b
He has spent all the money he was paid for us.

Psalm 35:7b
They dug a deep hole to catch me.

Proverbs 13:8a
The ransom of a person's life is their wealth.

Psalm 142:7a
Set me free from my prison.

Psalm 71:14a
I will always put my hope in you.

It has taken two hours to check at your friend's, but it is now quite clear that Sarah has sent a message explaining what has happened to her.

Return to page 55.

Once again, even though you're investigating the disappearance of his wife, Kevin doesn't appear that pleased to see you. He seems nervous and ill at ease. He paces up and down, barely glancing at the note. Finally he says, 'She's told us you shouldn't be involved, so why don't you just pack it in and go home?'

'Aren't you worried that she's being held somewhere?'

'Yes – no – she hasn't come to any harm, but if you keep meddling you might cause her trouble. I don't know what he – they – might do to her.'

The door-bell rings. 'Excuse me,' says Kevin and goes into the hall to answer it. On the coffee-table you can see an envelope addressed to Sarah. It's the letter you noticed when you went to see Kevin earlier.

- If you didn't grab the chance to read it then, you can do so now, by going to page 42. Of course, if Kevin were to return and find you reading Sarah's private post there'd be a frightful row. On the other hand, if you haven't already sneaked a look, you might be missing a major clue.

- If you don't want to risk opening the letter, read on here.

Kevin comes back looking even more alarmed than ever. 'Problems?' you enquire.

'No, er, no! Just someone, er, Bill, who calls here sometimes.'

Choose immediately:

- Whether to jump up, run out of the house and try to catch this Bill and discover exactly who he is and what he's doing there. To do this, go to page 56.

- Whether to leave the house and sit in your car to think over the state of the case and how far you've got. Time is passing and you ought to be getting near a solution. To do this, go to page 63.

You try to check how much money Sarah has

It's the weekend. The banks are closed. Even if they were open, the details of their customers' accounts are confidential and they would be most unlikely to reveal them to you as a private detective.

How can you find out about Sarah's money? You could ask her husband Kevin, but if he's in any way involved in her disappearance you might get a false answer. You could ask Anna, but the same problem applies – if she's in any way involved you might be given a wrong answer. The church newsletter contains a list of deacons including the church treasurer, William Lord. Bill? You decide to visit him and find out what you can.

William Lord is a pleasant man, in his late fifties. He welcomes you, tells you how worried he is about Sarah's disappearance and explains that he used to be an accountant. He has taken early retirement and now does the church accounts as a sort of hobby, to keep his hand in.

You realize that you're fishing for rather sensitive information, so you start by asking about church funds: 'The church has to find all its own money?'

'Basically, yes. We can apply to various trusts for grants but the bulk of our money is what members of the congregation give.'

'That has to cover the minister's salary?'

'Yes, we call it a stipend, an allowance. Perhaps calling it that disguises that it's very low pay compared to most salaries.'

'But a lot for a congregation to find, on top of the costs of the building ...?'

'And supporting the Baptist Missionary Society and other charities like the local housing association scheme for homeless people, yes. Here we have to raise more than £20 000 a year just to keep going and pay all the expenses.'

'How do you manage?'

'Well, some Christians give very generously, as much as a tenth of their income after tax. We ask our members to take part in planned giving – that means instead of putting their loose change on the collection plate, they sit down once a year and calculate how much they can afford to give. When people do that they often discover that they can give far more than they were doing previously. After all, being a Christian isn't just about what we believe. It's about how we live and give: money and time to the church and to other people. But I'm being a preacher now instead of the treasurer!'

'Does the church have any other income?'

'There are the collections at each Sunday service, and often at a funeral people don't bother with expensive flowers but ask for the money to be given to the church instead. Then just occasionally we get large donations.'

'In people's wills you mean?'

'Sometimes, though recently we had a big donation of £50 000, which will help a lot. The church meeting decided to give £10 000 of it to Christian Aid, £10 000 to the Baptist Housing Association and to bank the rest towards church expenses for the coming year.'

'Who gave you that? Was it from a will?'

'The donor's alive, but was very keen to remain anonymous.'

You decide to press on: 'Is he or she a member of the church, then?'

'Oh yes, very definitely.'

'Might it help me in my enquiry to know who in your church can just write a cheque for £50 000?'

'It might. That's what places me in the difficult position of not knowing whether to break a confidence and tell you who this anonymous person is. No-one else knows, not even the other deacons.'

'I can assure you that I wouldn't tell anyone else, unless it turns out to be relevant to the investigation.' William looks uneasy, and pauses to mop his brow with a large blue handkerchief covered with white spots. It's just like the hankies tramps in cartoons carry tied to a stick over their shoulder with their belongings in. He then blows his nose like a great trumpet and puts the handkerchief away.

'Well,' he says at last, lowering his voice, 'even if you knew everyone in the church and their incomes, I don't think you'd guess who the donor was.'

Have a try, then turn over the page to see if you were right.

61

William looks you right in the eye and says simply: 'It was the minister herself.'

'Do you know where she got that sort of money?'

'Yes, as it happens I do. It was a legacy from an elderly aunt in Scotland. She – the auntie – belonged to the Church of Scotland and was a great friend of her parish minister. She knew that ministers don't have a very high salary and she had no children of her own. Her only heir was this one niece who she was so proud of, so she willed her the lot.'

'The lot?'

'About £200 000.'

'Wow! Was Sarah pleased about this?'

'Well, yes and no. She didn't think it was right to blow it all on herself or her family. She was very aware that Jesus told the rich young man in the Bible to sell all he had and give the money to the poor. So she intended to give a lot of the money to charity, including the Baptist church here, but you can see why she wanted it kept anonymous.'

'How long ago was all this?'

'Not that long. Her aunt died about a year ago. Sarah must have had the money about three weeks before she disappeared, because I distinctly remember her telling me when she gave me the cheque that it was the first she'd spent of it.'

This visit and chat has taken an hour.

Add 1 hour to your time score.

• If you haven't shown Kevin Sarah's note, you can do so now, by going to page 58.

• Otherwise, return to Kevin's house on page 63 and sit in your car to think over what you've found out. Don't forget to think about 'Bill'.

62

You sit in your car

This isn't really where you want to be. It's now Sunday afternoon, and while you're sitting thinking, nothing's happening to push developments forward in the case. Or do you hold nearly all the solution in your grasp but haven't quite seen it yet? Do you know how Sarah was kidnapped? Do you know why she was kidnapped? Do you know who did it? Do you know where she is now? Of course you don't know all the answers! What would be useful would be ...

Wait a minute! While you've been sitting thinking, Kevin's rushed out of the house and is getting in his car. He's driving down the drive towards where you've parked opposite. Is it a rendezvous with the kidnapper? Is he going to hand over ransom money? Is that why he didn't want you to be involved? It would certainly explain why he was so fidgety. You quickly open your copy of *Private Eye* magazine and hold it so he can't see your face. He drives out and down the road past you. You start your car and follow him. The chase is on!

You follow Kevin through several turnings, across a cross-roads where you have to give way, and through traffic lights on amber. To your surprise you manage to keep up. Then, on the Chapeltown main street, he pulls into a parking space a few hundred metres in front of you. It's a 20 minute waiting area so he can't be intending to stop here for long.

But as you drive towards him, to your horror you see that the street is fully parked. There's no spare space for you. This never happens in detective films! What are you going to do?

Think quickly. Try to work out a possible solution, then turn to the next page.

63

Whatever solution you were thinking of, you decide you've got to drive a little way past Kevin so as not to attract suspicion. As soon as you have done that you stop, put your emergency lights on as if you've broken down, jump out of the car and lift the bonnet. While you pretend to be tinkering with the engine, you can watch where Kevin's going. He has crossed the road and is using a bank cash-machine. You can't see from where you are exactly what he's doing, but it's clear that he's drawing out money. The machine is taking quite a long time to deliver the money to him, presumably either because it's delivering a lot or because he hasn't managed to type in the right code number first time.

While he's doing this another car pulls up, double parking on the road opposite you, right next to Kevin. You see Kevin passing the money to the driver – there's no passenger. You can't see clearly who the driver is, as they're leaning away from you towards the passenger door, where Kevin is handing over the money. But you will see the mystery person better when they turn to drive off.

'Good afternoon. Having a spot of trouble?' You half hear a voice as you watch Kevin speaking nervously to the driver of the car, looking around suspiciously as he does so.

'Having trouble? Broken down?' You realize it's a voice on your side of the road speaking to you, and you turn round to see who it is, banging your head beautifully on the raised bonnet lid. A traffic warden is smiling at you helpfully.

'Er, I think I've got it going now. Er, fuel-pump problem,' you splutter.

'Like to get in and give it a try?'

You get in and – surprise, surprise! – the engine starts smartly without any trouble at all.

'Oh, er, thanks.' You wave to the warden and have no choice but to drive off. The car you were watching is already moving and Kevin is getting into his car. You can't see anything of the driver of the mystery car now as it's too far away.

You must choose quickly:

• Whether to follow Kevin and see where he drives now, by going to page 67.

• Whether to follow the mystery car, by going to page 68.

You find out about chapels of rest

You ring a colleague on the car-phone. This is what you're told.

Chapels of rest are used by funeral directors (or undertakers, as they used to be called) to keep bodies in until the funeral. Sometimes relatives visit them to 'pay their last respects', meaning to view the body prepared for the funeral and sort of say goodbye. Chapels of rest became more common after the custom of keeping the dead at home until the funeral died out. Part of the reason for this was more and more houses having lounge-diners, so that there was no longer anywhere to put dead bodies at home!

Closed churches can be adapted to be chapels of rest very easily and have the right atmosphere. They shouldn't be confused with 'ordinary' chapels. For example, most Baptists used to use the word 'chapel' instead of 'church' to describe the building where they worshipped. When older Baptists talk about going to chapel, they certainly aren't talking about being prepared for burial or cremation! A chapel of rest is for corpses.

But why would a corpse want a box of groceries?

You've lost the chance to catch up the mystery driver, but you can choose whether:

- To return to Ebenezer church in time for the Sunday evening service, by going to page 74.

- To investigate the chapel of rest, if you haven't already done so, by going to page 71.

You follow Kevin

He simply drives straight home again, puts the car away in the garage and goes back into the house.

You're stuck. The trail's dried up. It's Sunday evening. You feel hungry and rather depressed. You look at your watch and see that it's about a quarter of an hour to the Ebenezer evening service. That's an idea! You've got nothing to lose by going to it, and being right on the scene of the kidnapping might just help you to think out the crime further. After the service you might as well go home and get an early night.

Drive to page 74 for the Ebenezer evening service.

You follow the mystery car

This driver can't possibly know you're following him – or her! You wind your way through Chapeltown back streets until the mystery car stops outside what looks like a disused church. Above the doors you can see in the stonework the words PRIMITIVE METHODIST CHURCH 1875 but it's clear that the church closed some time ago, because a newer, painted notice by the door says WILLIAMSON BROTHERS CHAPEL OF REST.

The mystery driver has got out of the car and is carrying a large cardboard box in one hand while trying to find the key to the door with the other – without success. The driver has their back to you and is wearing a tatty anorak with the hood up, tracksuit trousers and trainers, so it's hard to tell much about them. You still can't even work out if this is a male or a female.

Next minute you see the box fall and groceries spill out of it onto the pavement – cornflakes, packet milk, biscuits, tea, tins of food. The person bends down to pick the items up, still with their back turned to you. Eventually everything is returned to the box, the door is unlocked and the mystery person goes in.

After about five minutes, the person comes out empty-handed. The box and its contents have been left inside the building. This time you get a front view. It's a tramp! Or rather, it looks like a tramp. Is this Bill? A bushy beard conceals most of the face. Whoever he is, he carefully re-locks the door. Then with just a glance from side to side to see whether anyone is watching or following on the street, he gets into the car and drives off.

Choose now whether:

• To stay here and investigate this chapel of rest, by going to page 71.

68

- To follow the car again and see where the driver goes now, by going to page 70.
- To find out what a chapel of rest is, if you're not sure, by going to page 66.

You follow the car again

The bearded, hooded figure drives off towards the town centre and you follow at what you hope is an unsuspicious distance. But you haven't gone more than half a mile when the Ecclesfield bus indicates right and pulls out in front of you. It's a double-decker and completely blocks your view of the car you're following. A twelve-year-old is staring at you from the upstairs back window rather rudely. You wonder whether to pull a face until you see a look-alike older face of someone who resembles a mixture between a heavyweight wrestler and an escaped murderer also staring out. It's his dad! You decide not to pull a face.

Eventually you arrive in a traffic queue leading to roadworks with temporary lights. It takes a long time for you to get through. By the time the bus pulls into a stop to pick up passengers, the car and its mystery occupant are nowhere in sight.

This means you have to choose whether:

• To go to the Ebenezer evening service, by turning to page 74.

• To find out about chapels of rest, by turning to page 66.

• To investigate the chapel of rest you've just come from, by going to page 71.

You investigate the chapel of rest

You cross the road and approach the double doors of the building. Gently you try to open them, but the mystery driver has locked them properly and you clearly can't get in. Not only that, but you feel a bit of a fool as a woman exercising her alsatian is watching you rather suspiciously while her dog decorates the pavement. You don't know which annoys you more, the stares of the owner or the products of the dog!

You leave owner and dog and walk down the side of the building in search of a back door. Weeds have overgrown the old church path to the back and several broken windows have been boarded up. There are broken drain-pipes and marks where rainwater has flowed down the walls from the guttering instead of down the pipes. The windows that remain aren't clear glass, but frosted like windows in a bathroom, so you have no way of seeing in. The paint has flaked off the window-frames leaving only a few patches that show it was once an unexciting brown colour.

At the back of the old chapel is an extension that looks as if it might have been built later as a kitchen for church teas and social events. But the door there is not only locked, but actually overgrown with moss and ivy. It's not been opened for years. So the front side that the public see is the best kept and most attractive, which doesn't say a lot, since the sides and back of the building are in deep decay.

You don't just look. As you tiptoe around the building you listen very carefully for any sign of life. You almost fall over a rusty dustbin, but you can hear nothing. Why would a carton of groceries including cornflakes and milk be taken into a building like this?

You walk round to the front again, but to your surprise the woman with the dog has been joined by a man, apparently her husband. They are both eyeing you very suspiciously so you decide to be open with them. You walk straight up and show them your Quicksolve identity card.

'I'm interested in who owns this building,' you explain, 'as part of an enquiry I'm making.'

'Well, we live next door but one,' says the woman. 'As a matter of fact my mother used to go to this church when it was a church. She was a Prim.'

'A Prim? You mean she was called Primrose and she changed her name?'

'Nah! "Prim" was short for "Primitive Methodist". She used to tell me proudly that that was a nickname as well – Primitive – because they went in for open-air preaching and ranting sermons, nothing posh or read from a book, but made up as you went along.'

'But it's a chapel of rest now?'

'No, it isn't. It used to be, until about a year ago, but it's been empty since, as far as we know.' Her husband nods.

'I've just seen someone go in there,' you explain.

'We've seen him too,' says the husband. 'He goes in there regularly twice a day, morning and evening, sometimes with boxes of food.'

'I think he's a tramp,' says his wife. 'He's always dirty looking, same old tatty clothes and bushy beard. I reckon he's living in there.'

'Funny thing is,' says the husband, 'he never seems to spend the night there.'

'And whoever's seen a tramp with a car?' his wife adds.

72

'Could be one of them squatters,' says the husband. 'We don't want them moving in on this street.'

'Have you ever seen lights on in the chapel? Or other people coming and going?'

'No, only him,' says the man. 'Though my next-door neighbour – he generally likes a good few jars at the pub – swears blind he saw a coffin being carried in there late at night the other week. So perhaps it's in use again as a chapel of rest after all.'

'Aye, well blind's the right word for how he comes back from the pub,' snorts the wife. 'You can't take no notice of his stories. He said he saw a flying saucer the week before, but I reckon it was the one his wife threw at him when he got home.'

You thank the couple very much for their help and go back to your car, walking through the dog mess on the way. Squelch! Ugh!

Choose now:

- Whether to head for the Ebenezer evening service, by going to page 74.

- Whether to find out about chapels of rest, if you haven't already done so, by going to page 66.

You go to the Ebenezer evening service

As you drive into the church car-park, to your surprise you see that your assistant has turned up with a flask and sandwiches in the hope of catching you here. This quick tea refreshes you and together you go into the service. The people at the door welcome you and give you a newsletter and notice sheet as they realize you're a visitor. The church is warm and comfortable and about half full, just as Anna described, and you sit near the back. The organist is playing chorus songs and hymns and people are joining in singing them or talking quietly before the service itself begins. The baptistry is of course covered. From the vestry or office door, into the church walks Anna. She stands at the front and the organ stops playing.

'Good evening and welcome everybody,' she says, 'and a special welcome to visitors here this evening. We hope you'll enjoy the service and that you'll sign

74

the visitors' book at the end. The theme of the service this evening is "God – Supplier of Our Needs". We begin with the hymn "The Magic Penny".'

In a second or two you're on your feet with the congregation singing the hymn. 'The Magic Penny' – it's a catchy tune. Your mind switches back to the missing minister and the reasons for her disappearance. Did she walk out on her family, as the police believe, or was it a kidnapping, for money? The song has ended and you sit with the rest of the congregation as Anna leads a prayer. You close your eyes but your concentration isn't good and only phrases of the prayer drift into your mind ...

'Thank you, Lord, for supplying our needs in so many ways: health and strength, "daily bread" – food and warmth, friends and family ... and for revealing your love to us supremely in your son Jesus ...' You open your eyes and peep at Anna. She isn't reading this prayer but is making it up as she goes along. Her own eyes are closed. '... and now we join together in saying the prayer he taught us, "Our Father ...".'

The Lord's Prayer now follows. At the end it is William Lord, the church treasurer, who walks to the front to read a passage from the Bible.

'The first reading this evening is taken from the First Letter to Timothy, chapter 6, on page 263 in the Bibles on the seats.' He waits for a few seconds for people to find the passage so they can follow what he reads.

'"Some people think that religion is a way to be rich. Well, religion does make a person very rich, if they are satisfied with what they have. What did we bring into this world? Nothing! What do we take out of the world? Nothing! Therefore if we have food and clothes, that ought to be enough for us. But many people want to get rich. They fall into temptation and are trapped in many foolish and harmful ideas which can lead to their downfall and destruction. For the love of money

75

is a source of all kinds of evil ...'" He carries on reading but you're thinking about the beginning of the passage, especially about the love of money.

Poor Sarah. She never wanted to be rich. A kidnapper does. It's three weeks now since she vanished. Anna has announced another hymn so you stand and start the first verse:

> God moves in a mysterious way
> His wonders to perform;
> He plants his footsteps in the sea,
> And rides upon the storm.

Mysterious ... in this very church at almost this very time Sarah disappeared. To solve the case you need to know who took her, why, and where she is now. Wouldn't it be a triumph if you could bring her back in the same stunning way in which she disappeared? You're on the last verse:

> Blind unbelief is sure to err,
> And scan his work in vain;
> God is his own interpreter,
> And he will make it plain.

Make it plain. Clear. Sitting down again you take out your notepad and write on it:

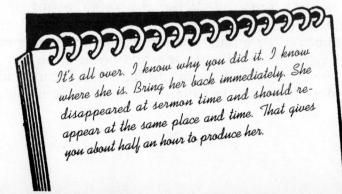

It's all over. I know why you did it. I know where she is. Bring her back immediately. She disappeared at sermon time and should re-appear at the same place and time. That gives you about half an hour to produce her.

It's a daring plan. You're going to send this note to the kidnapper and hope that it will convince them you know everything and that they will fetch Sarah for you. The only question is, are you sure who to send it to? You tear the sheet off the pad ready to give to your assistant. What are you going to do? Think carefully. A mistake now could cost you the entire case.

If you're going to ask your assistant to deliver your note at once, you must write down your solution to the case first, as you will be told the correct solution almost immediately. Remember, you need to get right:

• who is responsible for Sarah's disappearance,

• the reason for her disappearance,

• where she is now.

If you choose the last option listed below, you will have to **add 1 hour to your time score**. This is because you will have to wait till after the service for an opportunity to talk the case over with your assistant, but doing so may make your solution more likely to be correct.

• If you want your assistant to pass the note to Anna at the front, **write down your solution** then turn to page 79.

• If you want your assistant to pass it to William Lord, **write down your solution** then turn to page 78.

• If you want your assistant to pass it to John Ingram, the other deacon, **write down your solution** then turn to page 80.

• If you want your assistant to pop out and deliver it to Kevin, who is home on Sunday evenings, **write down your solution** then turn to page 82.

• If you want to save the note until you can go over the facts of the case again, turn to page 81.

Your assistant passes your note to William Lord

You watch him closely. He reads it, looks puzzled, then folds it up and places it in the pocket of his smart grey suit. He does not move from his seat, however.

You may now change your solution to the case if you wish. You also have the chance to scribble a copy of the note and send it to someone else.

- If you want your assistant to pass the note to Anna, turn to page 79.

- If you want your assistant to pass the note to John Ingram, turn to page 80.

- If you want your assistant to deliver the note to Kevin, turn to page 82.

- If you want to go over the facts of the case again after the service, turn to page 81.

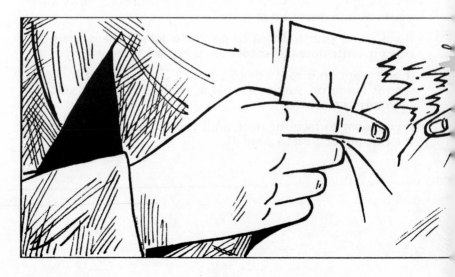

Your assistant passes your note to Anna

You watch Anna read it while another Bible passage is being read by John Ingram. She looks very angry and tears the note up, glancing in your direction as if she's wondering whether it's a joke in very poor taste.

You may now change your solution to the case if you wish. You also have the chance to scribble a copy of the note and send it to someone else.

- If you want your assistant to pass the note to William Lord, turn to page 78.

- If you want your assistant to pass the note to John Ingram, turn to page 80.

- If you want your assistant to deliver the note to Kevin, turn to page 82.

- If you want to go over the facts of the case again after the service, turn to page 81.

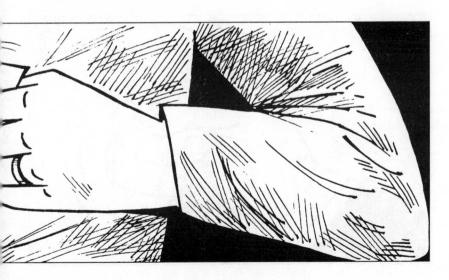

Your assistant passes your note to John Ingram

He sits and reads it, then looks around blankly as if to see who sent it and what it might possibly mean. He screws the note up and puts it in his pocket. But he doesn't do anything else.

You may now change your solution to the case if you wish. You also have the chance to scribble a copy of the note and send it to someone else.

- If you want your assistant to pass the note to William Lord, turn to page 78.

- If you want your assistant to pass the note to Anna, turn to page 79.

- If you want your assistant to deliver the note to Kevin, turn to page 82.

- If you want to go over the facts of the case again after the service, turn to page 81.

You go over the facts of the case again

Add 1 hour to your time score.

'What we've got to do,' you say to your assistant, 'is to answer certain questions.' You write them down and hand the list to your assistant:

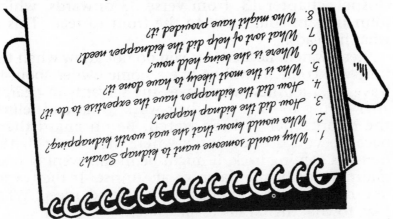

1. Why would someone want to kidnap Sarah?
2. Who would know that she was worth kidnapping?
3. How did the kidnap happen?
4. How did the kidnapper have the expertise to do it?
5. Who is the most likely to have done it?
6. Where is she being held now?
7. What sort of help did the kidnapper need?
8. Who might have provided it?

You talk through these questions with your assistant then phone the police and tell them what you think you know.

It is not necessary to name the kidnapper's accomplice correctly as part of your solution, though you do have an outside chance on this one. In fact, to close the case successfully you need not write down all eight answers, just three:

• who is responsible for Sarah's disappearance,

• the reason for her disappearance,

• where she is now.

When you have written down your solution to the case, go to the mirror on page 84 to check it.

Your assistant delivers the note to Kevin

This takes time, as you knew it would. After your assistant quietly leaves the church, more hymns are sung and prayers said. Church notices are given. Finally it's time for the Bible reading before the sermon. Anna announces a passage from Mark's Gospel, chapter 13, from verse 33 onwards, which John Ingram comes out to the front to read. This is what he reads:

'Keep watch. Be alert, for you do not know when the time will come. It will be like a home owner about to leave on a journey who leaves the servants in charge, after giving to each one their work to do and telling the doorkeeper to keep watch. Be on guard then, because you do not know when the owner of the house is coming back. It might be in the evening or at midnight or before dawn or at sunrise. If the owner returns suddenly, you must not be found asleep! What I say to you, then, I say to all: Watch!'

But you can't watch for anything because the lights have gone out. The church is in total darkness.

After some time of confusion and buzz of conversation, perhaps a minute or so, the lights come back on. Anna is looking stunned. John Ingram is standing with his mouth wide open and his Bible has fallen from his hands. 'Ahs' and 'Oohs' and gasps are coming from the congregation.

For there in the pulpit is a woman you haven't seen before. But you know from photographs you have seen at her home that it's Sarah. She looks pale, dazed, shaken, almost as surprised as the congregation are to see her there, but she's safe.

82

You slip away from the chaos and delight that has brought the service to a standstill, caused Anna to forget all about preaching the sermon, and brought the congregation out of their seats. People are running to the front to greet Sarah, shaking her hand, kissing, hugging, waving at her in delight.

Quietly leave the church and go to the mirror on page 84 to check the details of the solution to the case.

The Solution

Before the kidnap, Kevin's luxury-lift business was losing money massively and he had big debts. He had taken to gambling heavily in a stupid effort to gain money but only gained more debts. Remember the betting-slips? He kept these extra debts secret from Sarah. When Sarah inherited the £200 000, Kevin thought she would pay off all his debts and that he'd be able to enjoy gambling with the money that remained. He was horrified that she intended to give so much of the money away to charities. So, using his engineering expertise, he designed the tunnel, the trap-door in the pulpit and the hinge gear, and connected it into the church's electrical system.

On the day of the kidnap, while the children were in the bath before going to bed, Kevin slipped out of the house. Unseen by anyone, he hurried to the church, entered through the back door and switched off the lights during the last verse of the hymn before the sermon. The same switch released the trap-door in the pulpit and dropped Sarah down into the tunnel, where his accomplice was already concealed waiting to gag her and tie her up. Kevin ran home as soon as he'd put out the lights and was away for only a few minutes. The children didn't even know he'd gone out. Sarah didn't know Kevin was involved either, but later on it was he who allowed the accomplice to take her a Bible so she could read it in captivity.

When everyone in the church had gone home, the accomplice smuggled Sarah into the old chapel of rest in a coffin. This was seen only by a drunk passing by on the street. She was kept in the chapel and fed by the accomplice's daily delivery of groceries. She wanted to write to her husband to tell him she was safe, but he ordered the accomplice to say she could write to Anna

84

instead. The note could say she was safe in return for telling Anna to call off Quicksolve. Remember, it was Anna who called you in, not Kevin. Kevin didn't bother to read the note but let his accomplice deliver it to Anna.

Meanwhile, Kevin was using Sarah's cash card and PIN (personal identity number) to draw out her money. His accomplice was also making her sign blank cheques which he told her were for the use of the kidnapper. Of course, her cheque book wasn't in the pulpit with her in the service, but the accomplice said he'd broken into the house and taken it.

Kevin had the idea that once all Sarah's money had been transferred to him, a share would be given to the accomplice, who would vanish for ever. (All he had to do was destroy his false beard and tramp's false clothes and resume his normal identity.) Sarah would then be 'rescued' by Kevin arriving at the chapel of rest to release her, pretending he'd given all her money to the kidnappers. She would then always be grateful to him for arranging her release! That was the plan.

So the person responsible for Sarah's disappearance was her husband, Kevin. The reason for her disappearance was theft (or count money). The place where Sarah was kept was the disused chapel of rest.

The accomplice – and you didn't have to work this out to get the solution right – had to be someone Sarah didn't know. It was Kevin's business partner Bill Foster, equally in a mess because of the firm's problems. He appeared in disguise as Bill the tramp at the door of the manse in an effort to see Kevin. Bill wanted to check the tunnel and other details before the day of the kidnap. Instead, the door was answered by Sarah. She took pity on him and tried to sort out this 'tramp,' writing him into her personal organizer, much to his dismay.

Go to page 86 to work out your final score.

Working Out Your Final Score

Over the weekend, you have spent 16 hours working on the case **plus** the extra hours you chose to clock up or found you had to spend as the case went along.

First, calculate your total time score by adding 16 hours to the number of (extra) hours you have already noted down during the investigation. The maximum number of extra hours you may have spent is 10 hours and the minimum is 2 hours, because you couldn't avoid passing through two sections that made you add 1 hour to your time score. So your total time score will be between 18 and 26 hours.

Next, give yourself **1 penalty point** for each hour in your total time score.

Now add **10 penalty points** for each of the three parts of the solution you got **wrong**: the **person** responsible for Sarah's disappearance, the **reason** for her disappearance and the **place** where Sarah was. Do not add anything for parts you got right.

Your final score is your total number of penalty points. The lower it is, the better. In fact the minimum score is 18 penalty points.

- If you scored 21 penalty points or less, go to page 89.

- If you scored from 22 to 26 penalty points, go to page 88.

- If you scored 27 penalty points or more, go to bed. It's still weekend (just!) and you'll need some sleep before you can face the Boss in the morning. Better luck with your next job – making the tea in the office or changing to a new company called Slowsolve?

Working Out Your Final Score

Time Score

1 hour 2 hours 3 hours 4 hours

4+16= 20 hours = 20 penalty points

Solution

Person, reason right = no penalty points
Place wrong = 10 penalty points

Final Score

20 + 10 = 30 penalty points

'Hmmph,' says the Boss, reading your case notes, 'I suppose it's not that bad. Anyway, it gives you the chance to represent us at the celebration next weekend.'

'Next weekend?'

'Yes. It'll be a change from work. They're having three celebratory services, morning, afternoon and evening, with special preachers, on account of the minister's safe return. They're going to be extra long services of thanksgiving. There will be coffee after morning service, and a tea party at 4 p.m. between the afternoon and evening services. Oh, and they're holding a special prayer meeting after the evening service.'

'Couldn't you ... er, shouldn't you be there?' you ask the Boss.

'Love to be, but unfortunately I've booked a weekend away so you'll have to represent the firm. I've already told the church you're going. Jolly good. It'll be nice and relaxing for you after working all last weekend on the case.' You head for the door.

THE END

If you scored 21 penalty points or less

'Excellent work. Well done. Embarrassed the police. Helped the church. Done the firm good. First rate,' the Boss tells you. 'Come on, you've had to work all weekend, so the least I can do is buy you a decent lunch.'

You brighten up at this prospect. Within minutes you're sitting in a swish restaurant, slurping at your soup with another four courses and coffee to look forward to. The Boss is opposite you tucking into a heaped plate of spaghetti as his first course, and getting covered in sauce. You can hear a sort of bleeping sound and although your Boss is gobbling greedily, you didn't think indigestion could be so rhythmic: peep-peep, peep-peep, peep-peep. Really! But it's not indigestion, it's a pocket portaphone and soon the Boss is talking:

'Oh dear, so sorry to hear about that ... How distressing for you ... Yes, we have worked a lot for religious groups ... Yes, we were involved in the kidnap case in today's papers ... Certainly ... Right away ... In fact one of our best people is sitting with me now ... I'll send them right away ... Goodbye.' You know what's coming.

'Well, well. What a pity,' says the Boss with a smirk. 'We must do this again some other time. Look, I tell you what, I'll eat your lunch and you can get onto this new case right away. There's no time to lose. Goodbye.'

There's nothing left to say to the Boss except: 'Goodbye.'

THE END

Notes for Teachers

The Missing Minister can be used as a class library book in Key Stage 2 or to stretch able youngsters in this stage in RE. It can be used as part of the RE programme in Key Stage 3 or for lower-ability youngsters in Key Stage 4. It provides an opportunity to learn about Christian worship, beliefs and practice, and an opportunity to develop skills in evaluating evidence. It is intended to complement an earlier book in the series, *Sudden Death at the Vicarage*, which was in an Anglican setting, by providing a Free Church setting (see SCAA Model Syllabus 1, Christianity 3a, page 41).

Both National RE Model Syllabuses have as attainment targets 'Learning about Religions' and 'Learning from Religion' (*ibid.* page 7) and list as appropriate skills and processes: investigation, interpretation, reflection, empathy, evaluation, analysis, synthesis, application and expression. Most of these are addressed in this book, some in depth, e.g. evaluation and analysis. Where the book is being used in group work it will also encourage the identified attitudes (*ibid.* page 8) of fairness, respect and enquiry. Both National Model Syllabuses emphasize the distinctiveness of religions, and by treating religions separately, the books in this series emphasize the uniqueness of each religion, so that pupils might start to acquire 'a coherent understanding of individual religions' (*ibid.* page 6). But it is only a start.

Cross-curricular skills – careful reading, analysis of data and decision-making – are all required throughout the text, and although there are choices and decisions for readers to make, the text is looped in such a way that all readers will read most of the text at some point in their progress through the book.

In particular *The Missing Minister* can be used:

• to introduce Christianity in an unexpected way in Key Stage 3, dissolving some pupil expectations that RE is a predictably routine subject

• before interviewing a preacher, deacon, minister or lay representative of the Christian community as part of a unit on Christianity in RE, so that the experience of the interviewee can be compared with roles within the story

• to introduce or revise work on church buildings or Christian artefacts in a highly unusual way, perhaps before or after a class visit – in the text everyone visits the Baptist church as part of the detective trail

- to lead to an imaginative approach to studying places of worship and not merely a historical approach, providing an affective rather than a merely factual angle to learning in RE

- as an opportunity in Key Stage 3 for pairs or groups of youngsters to work together, negotiating paths to follow and discussing options as they progress through the case, and developing group-work skills in the process

- as a thriller for when the teacher is absent, to prevent classes from kidnapping the supply teacher and sending a ransom note to the member of staff in charge of organizing cover!

- as an absorbing homework task which youngsters will want to finish to see 'whodunnit'. Experience piloting the series suggests that youngsters will also go back after reaching the end to read the clues they've missed

- to address content identified in both National Model Syllabuses on the nature of the church or similar content in local agreed syllabuses for RE

- above all, to show that **RE can be fun!**

Using the genre of the mystery detective story, and a Free Church setting, the reader is introduced to various concept and content areas in RE:

- symbols in Baptist churches: baptistry, Communion table, pulpit, and why the symbolism is deliberately plain

- personnel: deacon, pastor/minister, the role and working life of a minister; the role of an area superintendent in Baptist churches

- Baptist beliefs and church organization

- believers' baptism

- the Christian Bible and its importance in faith and worship, including using a Bible and looking up references

- Christian worship in a Free Church setting, including the concept of a 'Free Church', the importance of the sermon, Communion

- Christians Together and an understanding of ecumenism in practice

- the activities of a Christian community (local church)
- cameos of C. H. Spurgeon and the Amish, plus brief references to John Bunyan and Martin Luther King

This book is **not** intended to replace systematic, careful study of Christianity or of churches or to provide a course on Christian worship. While the writer has tried to avoid stereotyping, in an RE lesson youngsters may need to be cautioned to avoid making generalizations. Clearly not all Christians would think, talk or behave as the ones in this **story** do.

Church and chapel
The use of these terms can be confusing. In a Victorian village, people were often labelled as 'church' (belonging to the Church of England) or 'chapel' (belonging to one of the Free Churches). Among stricter Baptists, the church was the gathered community of believers, the congregation were the people who actually attended worship and the chapel was the building. There is theological value to Christians in distinguishing the community from the building as 'going to church' has come to mean going to the church building. Many Free Church people still talk of 'going to chapel'. But because in everyday conversation, even among Free Church Christians, and certainly among non-Christians, 'church' is commonly used to describe the building, this usage has been adopted here.

A final note of caution to the teacher
One teacher told me that she wondered why, while working on an earlier book in the series, so many youngsters kept asking if they could go to the toilet. It was some time before she realized that toilets have mirrors and they were trying to cheat on the solution by taking the book with them. Be warned!